AMAZING SIGHTS IN THE SKY

AURORAS

by Jane P. Gardner

Ideas for Parents and Teachers

Pogo Books let children practice reading informational text while introducing them to nonfiction features such as headings, labels, sidebars, maps, and diagrams, as well as a table of contents, glossary, and index.

Carefully leveled text with a strong photo match offers early fluent readers the support they need to succeed.

Before Reading

- "Walk" through the book and point out the various nonfiction features. Ask the student what purpose each feature serves.
- Look at the glossary together. Read and discuss the words.

Read the Book

- Have the child read the book independently.
- Invite him or her to list questions that arise from reading.

After Reading

- Discuss the child's questions. Talk about how he or she might find answers to those questions.
- Prompt the child to think more. Ask: Did you know Earth acts like a magnet before you read this book? What more would you like to learn about the magnetic field and how it plays a role in auroras?

Pogo Books are published by Jump!
5357 Penn Avenue South
Minneapolis, MN 55419
www.jumplibrary.com

Library of Congress Cataloging-in-Publication Data

Names: Gardner, Jane P., author.
Title: Auroras / Jane P. Gardner.
Description: Minneapolis, MN: Pogo Books, [2021]
Series: Amazing sights in the sky | Includes index.
Audience: Ages 7-10 | Audience: Grades 2-3
Identifiers: LCCN 2020004420 (print)
LCCN 2020004421 (ebook)
ISBN 9781645275657 (hardcover)
ISBN 9781645275664 (paperback)
ISBN 9781645275671 (ebook)
Subjects: LCSH: Auroras–Juvenile literature.
Classification: LCC QC971.4 .G37 2021 (print)
LCC QC971.4 (ebook) | DDC 538/.768–dc23
LC record available at
https://lccn.loc.gov/2020004420
LC ebook record available at
https://lccn.loc.gov/2020004421

Editor: Jenna Gleisner
Designer: Anna Peterson

Photo Credits: ginger_polina_bublik/Shutterstock, cover; Stastny_Pavel/Shutterstock, 1; oorka/Shutterstock, 3; Krissanapong Wongsawarng/Shutterstock, 4-5; muratart/Shutterstock, 6-7; FlashMovie/Shutterstock, 8-9 (sun), 10-11 (sun); NikoNomad/Shutterstock, 8-9 (planets); adventtr/iStock, 11 (Earth); sixfournorth, 12-13; Mike Beauchamp/iStock, 14-15; Mikko83/Shutterstock, 16-17; Petri jauhiainen/Shutterstock, 18-19 (top); SKY2014/iStock, 18-19 (bottom); Fotos593/Shutterstock, 20-21; vichie81/Shutterstock, 23 (left); Andrew Peacock/iStock, 23 (right).

Printed in the United States of America at Corporate Graphics in North Mankato, Minnesota.

TABLE OF CONTENTS

CHAPTER 1

LIGHTS IN THE NIGHT SKY

In the far north, above the ice and polar bears, the sky puts on a show. Colors streak across the night sky. This light show is an **aurora**.

Auroras in the **Northern Hemisphere** are called aurora borealis. We also call them northern lights. Those south of the **equator** are called aurora australis or southern lights.

Auroras can be viewed from outer space! What causes these beautiful colors? The sun and Earth both play a part. Let's take a look!

CHAPTER 2

SOLAR WIND AND MAGNETIC FIELD

The sun has an **atmosphere**. It is extremely hot. Gas **particles** flow out of it. These make up the **solar wind**.

sun

gas particles

The solar wind is fast. It streams at a speed of 500 miles (800 kilometers) per second! It rushes past the planets and their moons. It has been found far into the **solar system**. It even goes past the planet Uranus!

But Earth is protected from it. How? Earth has layers. The **core** is at the center. It is iron. This creates a **magnetic field**. It is invisible. But it shields Earth from most of the solar wind.

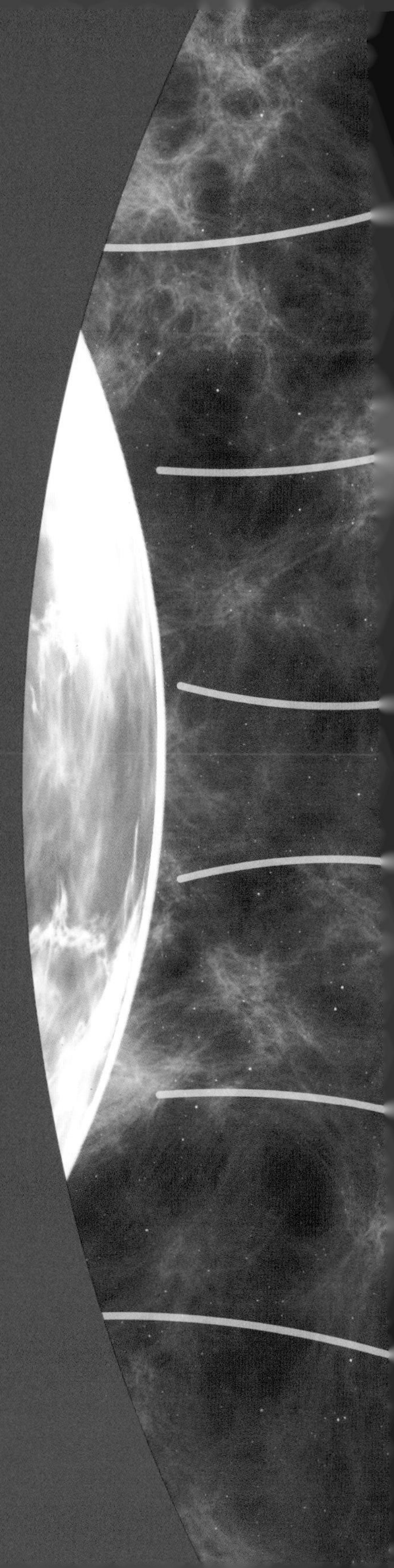

DID YOU KNOW?

What if Earth didn't have a magnetic field? The solar wind would slowly strip away Earth's atmosphere. It might take millions of years. But life on Earth would slowly disappear.

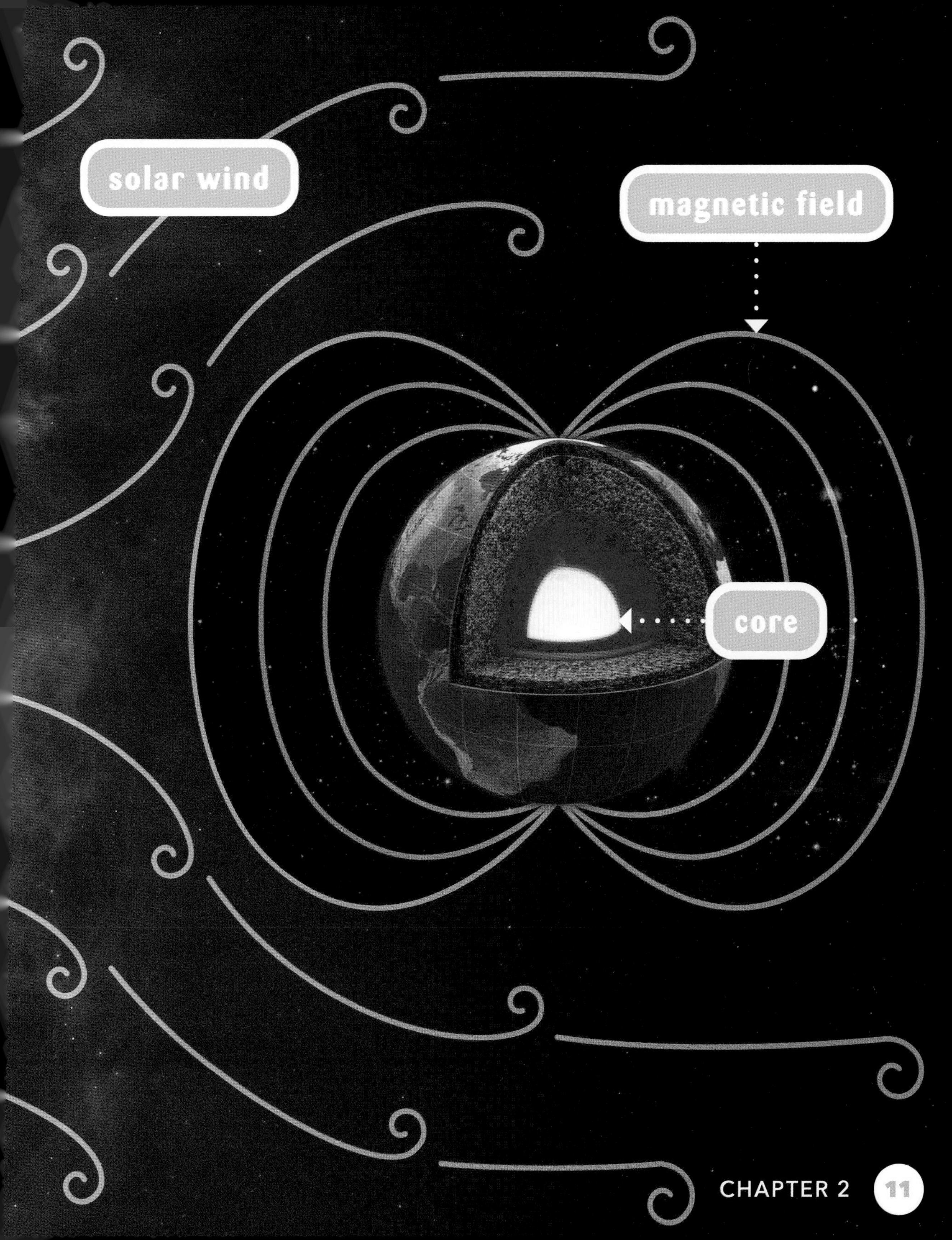
solar wind
magnetic field
core

Not all solar wind particles are blocked. Some enter the atmosphere. This happens near the North and South Poles. Why? Earth's magnetic field is weakest at the poles.

What happens when particles break through? They hit gases in Earth's atmosphere. This releases **energy**. The result is swirls of colorful light. If the solar wind hits **oxygen** gas, the aurora looks yellow, green, or red.

TAKE A LOOK!

How do auroras form? Take a look!

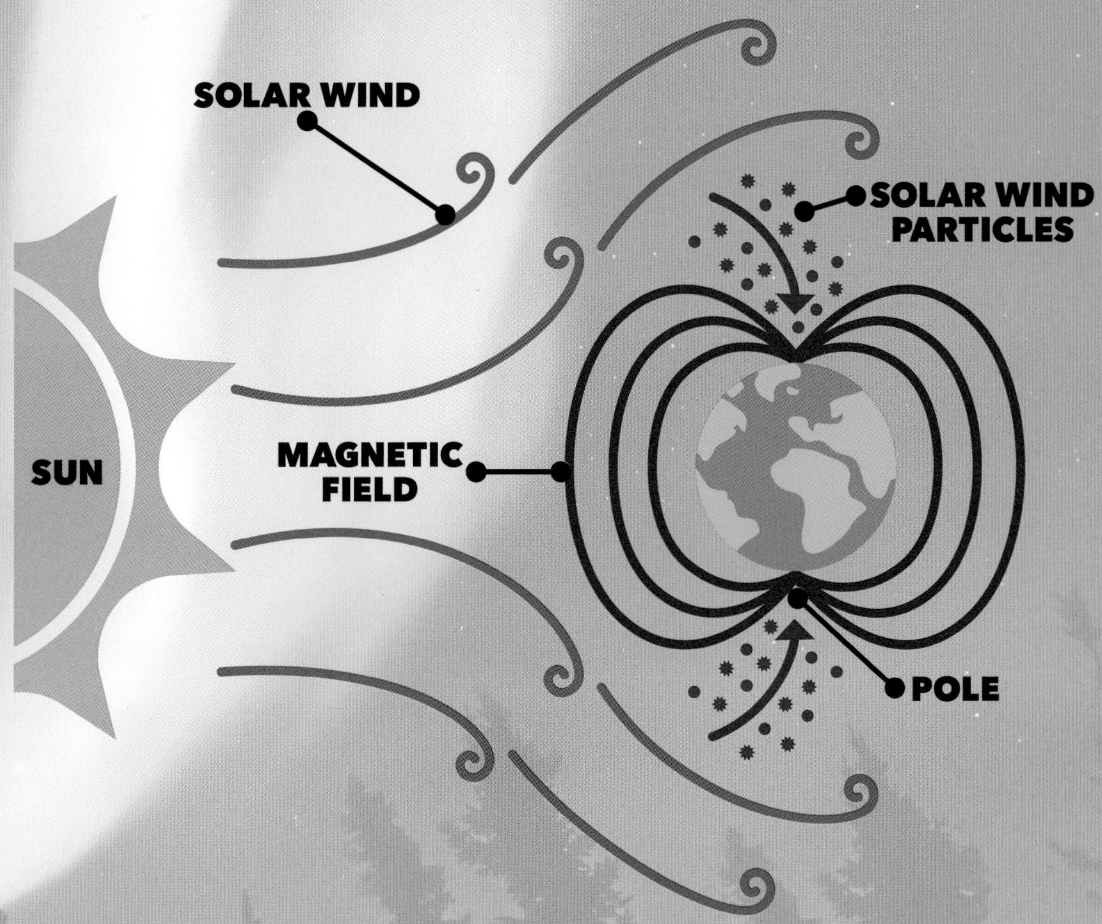

1. Solar wind blows from the sun toward Earth.
2. The magnetic field shields Earth from most of the solar wind.
3. At the poles, some solar wind particles enter Earth's atmosphere and create energy.
4. The energy created gives off light. It makes an aurora.

If the solar wind hits **nitrogen**, the aurora looks blue or purple. Earth's atmosphere is a mixture of gases. This is why the auroras we see are multicolored.

DID YOU KNOW?

Jupiter, Saturn, Uranus, and Neptune all have magnetic fields. What does this mean? These planets experience auroras, too!

CHAPTER 3

A CLOSER LOOK

Auroras appear to swirl. They mix and change shape. Why? The solar wind is fairly constant. It streams into the upper atmosphere regularly.

In fact, auroras are visible nearly every night. But only if you are in the right locations. You are most likely to see an aurora near the poles. The Arctic is a popular spot to see them. So is the Antarctic Circle.

You don't have to be near the poles to see auroras. They have even been seen in Honolulu, Hawaii. It is rare. But it happens! An aurora is an amazing sight to see. Would you like to see these swirls of color?

DID YOU KNOW?

Auroras aren't just lights. People have described hearing crackling or clapping noises. Why does this happen? Particles from the sun get trapped in the upper atmosphere. They release sound and light!

ACTIVITIES & TOOLS

TRY THIS!

MAKE A MAGNETIC FIELD

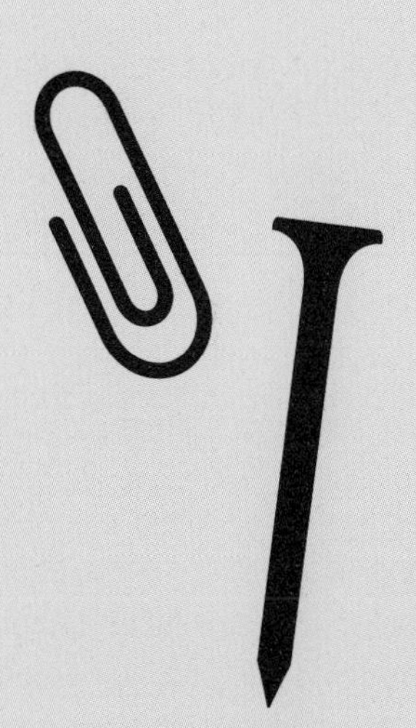

Earth and other planets act as magnets. With the help of an adult, you can make your own mini magnetic field! Be careful! The wire can get hot.

What You Need:

- insulated wire
- wire strippers
- nail
- one AA battery
- paper clip

1. **With the help of an adult, strip the protective coating off the wire with the wire strippers.**
2. **Wrap the wire tightly around the nail.**
3. **Touch one end of the wire to the negative end (-) of the battery.**
4. **Touch the other end of the wire to the positive end (+). The nail is now a magnet!**
5. **Move the paper clip near the magnet. Watch how they line up in the magnetic field.**

GLOSSARY

atmosphere: The mixture of gases that surrounds a planet or celestial body.

aurora: A luminous phenomenon that consists of light appearing in the upper atmosphere of a planet's magnetic polar regions.

core: The central part of Earth that is very hot.

energy: Power from a source that produces light and heat.

equator: An imaginary line around the middle of Earth that is an equal distance from the North and South Poles.

magnetic field: The part of space in which magnetic forces can be found. It extends from Earth's core and into outer space, where it interacts with the solar wind.

nitrogen: A gas that makes up much of the air in Earth's atmosphere.

Northern Hemisphere: The half of Earth that is north of the equator.

oxygen: The most common element found on or in Earth that makes up air and part of Earth's atmosphere.

particles: Extremely small pieces of something.

solar system: The sun together with the planets, many moons, asteroids, and comets that move in orbit around it.

solar wind: The continuous flow of charged particles that ejects from the sun's surface and into outer space.

INDEX

TO LEARN MORE

Finding more information is as easy as 1, 2, 3.

1. Go to www.factsurfer.com
2. Enter "auroras" into the search box.
3. Click the "Surf" button to see a list of websites.